THE **TESTING** SERIES

PARAMEDIC
INTERVIEW
QUESTIONS
& ANSWERS

THE **TESTING** SERIES
expert advice on test preparation

how2become

Orders: Please contact How2become Ltd, Suite 2, 50 Churchill Square Business Centre, Kings Hill, Kent ME19 4YU.

You can also order via the email address info@how2become.co.uk or through Gardners books at Gardners.com.

ISBN: 9781907558344

First published 2012

Typeset for How2become Ltd by Molly Hill, Canada.

Printed in Great Britain for How2become Ltd by CMP (uk) Limited, Dorset.

CONTENTS

INTRODUCTION BY RICHARD MCMUNN

Dear Paramedic Applicant,

Before you start reading the interview questions, tips and advice that are contained within this workbook, I wanted to tell you a little bit about my background and why I am qualified to help you.

I have spent 20 years in both the Armed Forces and the Fire Service, during which time I have been heavily involved in recruitment and training. I have worked with many Paramedics during my time and also have many contacts in the Paramedic recruitment sector. The advice that I will provide you within this workbook will be invaluable in your pursuit to becoming a Paramedic.

Whatever I have achieved in life I have done it through sheer hard work and determination. You will not pass the interview unless you put in plenty of preparation. I urge you to work hard in the build-up to the Paramedic interview and also consider attending my 1 day Paramedic Selection process training course, details of which you can find at the following link:

WWW.PARAMEDICCOURSE.CO.UK

If you have any questions, you can contact me at info@how2become.co.uk.

Best wishes,

Richard McMunn

CHAPTER 1:
MY FORMULA FOR SUCCESS

Over the last 20 years I have used the same formula time and time again to pass interviews. Over the next few pages and chapters I will explain what this formula involves, and more importantly how you can use it to assist you during every interview that you attend. The formula itself is a simple one, and is broken down into three different sections:

- Interview technique
- Research
- Responding to the interview questions

INTERVIEW TECHNIQUE

During my pre-interview preparation, I will concentrate on developing my interview technique. This will involve concentrating on the following key areas:

- Creating a positive first impression
- Presentation
- Effective communication
- Body language and posture

- Final questions
- Creating a positive final impression

Let's now break down each of these areas and look at them in detail.

CREATING A POSITIVE FIRST IMPRESSION

An interview panel will naturally create a first impression of you. As soon as you walk into the interview room they will be forming an opinion. Therefore, it is important that you get off on the right foot. Whenever I walk into any interview room I will always follow this process:

Knock before I enter the room

↓

Walk into the interview room standing tall and smiling

↓

Stand by the interview chair and say
"Hello, I'm Richard, pleased to meet you."

↓

Shake the hand of each interviewer firmly, whilst looking them in the eye

↓

Sit down in the interview chair, only when invited to do so

↓

Sit in the interview chair with an upright posture and with my hands resting palms facing downwards on the top of my knees, feet firmly on the floor

By following the above process I will be creating a positive first impression and demonstrating good qualities such as manners, self-discipline, politeness and motivation.

PRESENTATION

Presentation effectively means how I intend to dress for the interview, and also how I intend to come across. I want the interview panel to see me as a professional, motivated, conscientious and caring person who is taking the interview very seriously.

Some interviews, especially those in the public sector, do not require you to dress formally. For some bizarre reason, some senior managers believe that a person should not be assessed on how they present themselves at interview. Personally, I disagree with this approach. Whilst I agree there is no need to go out and buy an expensive suit or new pair of shoes, I do believe that a potential employee should make an effort in their appearance.

For the interview I will make sure that my suit is cleaned and pressed, my shoes are polished, and my personal hygiene is up to standard. This means simple things such as taking a shower, shaving, having a haircut and general grooming. I will always avoid brightly coloured clothes and generally go for a conservative approach such a dark blue, black or grey suit. If I do decide to wear any brighter, more vibrant colours, then this will be in form of a tie. I would strongly advise that you avoid brightly coloured socks or ties with cartoon characters on them!

A GOOD APPLICANT

A good applicant is someone who has taken the time to prepare. They have researched both the organisation they are applying to join and also the role that they are being interviewed for. They may not know every detail about the organisation and the role but it will be clear that they have made an effort to find out important facts and information. They will be well presented at the interview and they will be confident, but not overconfident. As soon as they walk into the interview room they will be polite and courteous and they will sit down in the interview chair only when invited to do so. Throughout the interview they will sit upright in the chair and communicate in a positive manner. If they do not know the answer to a question they will say so and they won't try to waffle. At the end of the interview they will ask positive questions about the job or the organisation before shaking hands and leaving.

A POOR APPLICANT

A poor applicant could be any combination of the following. They will be late for the interview or even forget to turn up at all. They will have made little effort to dress smartly and they will have carried out little or no preparation. When asked questions about the role they will have little or no knowledge. Throughout the interview they will appear to be unenthusiastic about the whole process and will look as if they want the interview to be over as soon as possible. Whilst sat in the interview chair they will slouch and fidget. At the end of the interview they will try to ask clever questions that are intended to impress the panel.

IMPROVING INTERVIEW TECHNIQUE

How you present yourself during the interview is important. Whilst assessing candidates for interviews I will not only assess their responses to the interview questions but I will also pay attention to the way they present themselves. A candidate could give excellent responses to the interview questions but if they present themselves in a negative manner then this can lose them marks.

In the build-up to your interview practise a few mock interviews. Look to improve your interview technique as well as working on your responses to the interview questions.

EFFECTIVE COMMUNICATION

Effective communication is all about how you speak to the interview panel, and also how you listen to what they have to say.

When responding to the interview questions you should speak clearly and concisely, avoiding all forms of waffle, slang or hesitations such as 'erm'. Look at each interview panel member when answering each question. Even though an interview question will be asked by one member of the panel at a time, you should always respond to the entire panel collectively. Look them in they eyes when speaking to them but never stare them out. This will only portray you in an aggressive or confrontational manner.

If you are unsure about a response to an interview question then just be honest. Consider saying something along the lines of:

"I'm sorry I do not know the answer to that question. I will look the answer up as soon as I get back home and contact you to let you know the answer."

If they accept this response, make sure you do research the response and contact them to let them know.

When the interview panel are speaking to me, or if they are asking me a question, I will always demonstrate good listening skills. This means that I will use facial expressions to show that I am taking on-board what they are saying and I will also nod to show them that I understand the question(s).

BODY LANGUAGE AND POSTURE

Whilst sat in the interview I will always make a conscious effort to sit upright and not slouch in the chair. I personally like to use my hands to emphasise points when responding to the questions but I will be careful not to overdo it. Even if the interview is going great and you are building up a good rapport with the panel, don't let your standards drop. Always maintain good body language and posture for the duration of the interview.

FINAL QUESTIONS

Before I attend the interview I will always think of two questions to ask the panel at the end. However, don't be trapped in the thinking that you must ask questions. It is acceptable to say:

"Thank you but I don't have any questions. I have already carried out lots of research and you have answered some of my questions during the interview."

Some people believe that you must ask three, four or even five questions at the end of the interview – this is total nonsense. Remember that the interview panel will have other people to interview and they will also need time to discuss your performance.

If you do decide to ask questions then make sure they are relevant.

CREATING A POSITIVE FINAL IMPRESSION

I have already discussed this during a previous section. I believe that a final positive statement can work wonders:

"I just want to say thank you for inviting me along to interview. I've really enjoyed the experience and I have learnt a tremendous amount about your company. If I am successful then I promise you that I will work very hard in the role and I will do all that I can to surpass your expectations."

RESEARCHING THE ROLE AND THE COMPANY

I highly recommend you try to visit the company or organisation you are applying to join. This serves a number of purposes but the most important are demonstrating commitment and dedication to the potential employer but also assisting you in your preparation for the interview.

Other great ways to find out about a particular company are by visiting their website, if they have one. Look for their 'mission statement', 'goals or 'values' and try to learn them to understand what they are all about and where they are going. Another effective research method is to type the company's name into a search engine such as Google or Yahoo. This should bring up a number of links for you to research.

Make sure that the information you read is current and up to date, and don't waste time reading items that are more than a year old as you will most probably find that they have changed since then.

TOPICS YOU SHOULD RESEARCH

You can spend many weeks studying different topics, but the following areas should be a priority in your research plan:

- Do they offer any development programmes for their employees, e.g. Investors in People?
- When were they established?
- Is it a large company and do they have overseas interests?
- Who are their customers and who are their major competitors?
- Where are they located, who is their Chief Executive and who are the shareholders?
- What are their short, medium and longterm goals?
- What are their values and policies?
- What are their products?
- Do they have a mission statement or vision?

Top tip
Only research things that are relevant and don't waste time reading irrelevant articles. Use your time wisely.

RESPONDING TO THE INTERVIEW QUESTIONS

The majority of interviews will contain two different types of questions. There will normally be motivational questions and situational questions. Here's an explanation as to how they differ.

MOTIVATIONAL QUESTIONS

Motivation interview questions are questions that are designed to assess the reasons why you want the job, what you have to offer, how much research you have done and also why you are the best candidate for the job. Whilst they are relatively easy to prepare for, you should still spend plenty of time getting your responses ready to the perceived motivational interview questions as these can, and often do, catch people out. Here's a list of sample motivational interview questions.

Q. Tell us a about yourself.

Q. Talk me through your CV.

Q. Why do you want this job?

Q. What do you have to offer?

Q. What skills do you have that would be of benefit in this role?

Q. Why should we give you the job and not the next candidate?

Q. I don't think you're experienced enough for this job. Convince me otherwise.

Q. What have you done to find out about this company and the role that you are applying for?

Q. How do you define success?

Q. What will you do if you are unsuccessful today?

You will see from the above list that the questions are very much aimed at your 'motivation' for wanting to join their company. Before you attend the interview I would suggest that you prepare responses for all of the above questions.

SITUATIONAL QUESTIONS

Situational interview questions are slightly harder to respond to. In order to determine the type of situational interview question you could be asked, I would recommend that you get a copy of the person specification or job description for the role. Once you have this to hand, you will then be able to prepare responses to the type of situations that you will be expected to perform within the role. The key to scoring high during your responses to this type of questioning is to provide evidence of where you have already been in this type of situation.

The following is a list of situational interview questions that I recommend you prepare for.

Q. Give an example of where you have worked as part of a team to achieve a difficult goal or task.

Q. Give an example of where you have provided excellent customer service.

Q. Give an example of where you have dealt with a customer complaint. What did you do and say?

Q. Give an example of where you have carried out a task despite pressure from others.

Q. Give an example of where you have made a difficult decision despite objection from other people.

Q. Give an example of where you have taken onboard constructive criticism.

Q. Give an example of where you have dealt with a difficult or aggressive customer.

Q. Give an example of where you have resolved an issue with a work colleague.

STAR METHOD

The STAR method is one that I have used during my preparation for many interviews in the past. It works most effectively when preparing responses to situational type interview questions. I would certainly recommend that you try using it.

The STAR method basically ensures that your responses to the interview questions follow a concise logical sequence and also that you cover every possible area. Here's a breakdown of what it actually means:

Situation – At the commencement of my response I will explain what the situation was and who else was involved. This will be a relatively comprehensive explanation so that the interviewer fully understands what it is I am trying to explain.

Task – I will then explain what the task was. This will basically be an explanation of what had to be done and by whom.

Action – I will then move on and explain what action I specifically took, and also what action other people took.

Result – I will finally explain what the result was following my actions. It is important to make sure that the result was positive as a result of your actions.

Have a go at using the STAR method when creating responses to the perceived interview questions. Write down the question at the top of a sheet of paper and write down each individual element underneath it.

CHAPTER 2
HOW TO PREDICT THE INTERVIEW QUESTIONS

During this section of the guide I am going to provide you with a useful strategy for predicting the interview questions.

The first stage of the process I am going to teach you is to obtain a copy of the job description for becoming a paramedic. You should be able to obtain a copy of this important document from the website of the NHS trust you are applying to join.

The following is a sample generic job description for a paramedic.

SAMPLE PARAMEDIC JOB DESCRIPTION

Paramedics work in rapid response ambulance units to deal with medical emergencies. Such emergencies may include minor injuries, sudden illness, and casualties arising from road and rail accidents, criminal violence, fires and other incidents. Paramedics are usually the first senior healthcare professionals on the scene and they assess the patient's condition and initiate specialist medical treatment and care before admission to hospital.

The primary goal of paramedics is to meet people's immediate treatment needs. They resuscitate and stabilise patients by using advanced life support techniques, administer drips, drugs and oxygen, and apply splints, and also assist with complex hospital transfers.

TYPICAL WORK ACTIVITIES

Paramedics deal with a wide range of patients who may be suffering from a variety of complaints. The response of a paramedic may vary but typical work activities include:

- responding to 999 calls for medical assistance at accidents, emergencies and other related incidents, usually in an ambulance with an ambulance technician to assist;
- assessing the condition of patients who are injured or taken ill suddenly;
- deciding what action is needed and initiating treatment;
- applying splints to limbs, dressing wounds, administering pain relief, oxygen, drips and fluids;
- using various kinds of equipment, including ventilators to assist breathing and defibrillators to treat heart failure, in order to resuscitate and stabilise patients;
- carrying out certain surgical procedures when necessary, such as intubation (insertion of a breathing tube);
- monitoring the patient's condition using high-tech equipment;
- assessing whether and how to move patients;
- liaising with members of other emergency services, such as the police or fire brigade;
- dealing with members of the public and family members present at the scene;
- treating patients in the ambulance while they are being transferred to hospital from the scene, or between hospitals in the case of patients being moved to receive specialist care;

- driving and crewing an ambulance or other rapid response vehicle;

- cleaning, decontaminating and checking vehicles and equipment to maintain a state of operational readiness;

- assisting with patient care in hospitals or health care centres;

- writing up case notes and reporting the patient's history, condition and treatment to relevant hospital staff.

You will note from the above job description that there are a number of important elements to the role. From this document we are able to predict the interview questions.

The NHS trust creates the job description for a specific reason – it is basically the 'blue-print' for the job of a paramedic. Before they take you on in the role they will want to hear evidence of where you have already carried out similar tasks in a previous role. If you have already carried similar tasks in a previous role then you are far more likely to succeed in the role of a paramedic.

I will now break down the above job description and provide you with sample interview questions taken from each 'typical work activity' bullet point.

TYPICAL WORK ACTIVITY

- ***responding to 999 calls for medical assistance at accidents, emergencies and other related incidents, usually in an ambulance with an ambulance technician to assist.***

Interview questions

Q. Provide details of where you have remained calm in a pressurised situation.

Q. Provide details of where you have taken the initiative to take action in a difficult and pressurised situation.

Q. What skills do you think are required when driving to an emergency incident in an Ambulance?

Q. What considerations would you give when driving to an emergency incident in an Ambulance during wet and icy conditions?

TYPICAL WORK ACTIVITY

- *assessing the condition of patients who are injured or taken ill suddenly.*

Q. How would you change your approach when treating and assessing a child during an emergency incident?

Q. What would you consider before treating a casualty who you suspected was drunk or under the influence of drugs?

TYPICAL WORK ACTIVITY

- *deciding what action is needed and initiating treatment.*

Q. Provide an example of where you have resolved a difficult and complex task.

Q. Provide an example of where you have carried out a risk assessment.

Q. How do you organise a typical working days activities?

Q. What would you consider when treating a casualty who was from a different religion or ethnic background to yourself?

TYPICAL WORK ACTIVITY

- *using various kinds of equipment, including ventilators to assist breathing and defibrillators to treat heart failure, in order to resuscitate and stabilise patients.*

Q. Provide an example of where you have had to learn new and complex equipment or procedures.

TYPICAL WORK ACTIVITY

- **assessing whether and how to move patients.**

Q. What considerations would you take into account before moving a casualty?

TYPICAL WORK ACTIVITY

- **liaising with members of other emergency services, such as the police or fire brigade.**

Q. Give an example of where you have worked with other teams in order to achieve a difficult task.

TYPICAL WORK ACTIVITY

- **dealing with members of the public and family members present at the scene.**

Q. Give an example of when you have delivered a difficult or stressful message to a group of people.

Q. Give an example of when you have had to calm a person down during a difficult of stressful situation. What did you do and what were your considerations?

TYPICAL WORK ACTIVITY

- **treating patients in the ambulance while they are being transferred to hospital from the scene, or between hospitals in the case of patients being moved to receive specialist care.**

Q. Give an example of when you have had to carry out a difficult task under pressure.

TYPICAL WORK ACTIVITY

- *driving and crewing an ambulance or other rapid response vehicle.*

Q. How do you think driving to an emergency incident differs from everyday normal driving?

Q. What would you have to consider when driving to an emergency incident using blue lights and sirens?

TYPICAL WORK ACTIVITY

- *cleaning, decontaminating and checking vehicles and equipment to maintain a state of operational readiness.*

Q. Give an example of when you have been responsible for maintaining an important item of equipment or piece of work.

TYPICAL WORK ACTIVITY

- *writing up case notes and reporting the patient's history, condition and treatment to relevant hospital staff.*

Q. Give an example of when you have had to take down important notes relating to a work related subject.

The above method of predicting the interview questions is an ideal way of preparing for your interview. The lesson here is simple – make sure that you obtain a copy of the job description and person specification for the role you are applying for. You will then be able to predict the interview questions using the above method demonstrated.

CHAPTER 3
SAMPLE INTERVIEW QUESTIONS AND ANSWERS

The type of interview questions you will be asked by the panel will very much depend on the service or trust you are applying to join. However, the interview will predominantly be based around the following areas:

- The application form and your responses;
- The reasons why you want to join their Ambulance Service;
- What you know about their Ambulance Service;
- What you know about the role you are applying for and the qualities required performing it competently;
- Your skills, experiences and qualifications that relate to the role;
- What you think the job involves;
- How you deal with difficult situations;
- Your knowledge and understanding of diversity and community awareness;
- What the training involves in order to successfully qualify in the role.

The interview will normally be carried out by two people, depending on the service you are applying to join. For example, some Ambulance Services will use a human resources officer and a duty station officer to carry out the interview, which will last up to one hour in duration.

On the following pages I have provided a number of sample interview questions and responses. The responses I have provided are for illustration purposes only and they should not be used during your own interview. Be sure to create responses to the questions based on your own skills and experiences.

Q1 - CAN YOU TELL US ABOUT OUR TRUST?

Tip – this question is virtually guaranteed so make sure you research thoroughly the trust that you are applying to join. The following is a very good response from a previously successful candidate. Use it as a basis for constructing your own response to this question based on the trust that you are applying for.

(Sample response based on the London Ambulance Service)

The LAS is a 24/7 365 days a year service and is governed by a trust board which consists of 12 members. The Chief executive is Peter Bradley and he joined in May 1996. He had taken over from Martin Gorham and took his ideas and policies and improved them. He also brought in the consultation meetings to empower the staff and improve the service. LAS have over 4500 employees across the 70 stations and 5 headquarters, which cover approximately 620 square miles. With regards to vehicles, you have around 400 ambulances and 200 response cars. LAS targets are to get to 75% CAT A calls within 8 minutes, 95% CAT B calls within 19 minutes which overall are being met and this year LAS have attended over a million calls. LAS doesn't just respond to emergency calls, it also has PTS and A & E support roles to help with the non-life threatening calls and day to day transfers to and from hospital. With regards to the future, LAS are intending to submit the application to become a foundation trust, and have also been taking steps to reduce your environmental impact, by recycling at 90% of your sites, fitting LED lights to vehicles and introducing the bicycle loan scheme. You will also be building a new ambulance station for the 2012 Olympics. A new system that is being developed called CAD2010 will allow you handle calls and dispatch staff and vehicles more efficiently. The LAS is also involved in community safety partnerships, which involves taking a multi-agency approach and talking with other emergency services and councils to gain community awareness and planning for major incidents.

Q2 – HOW WOULD YOU CHANGE YOUR ATTITUDE/APPROACH WHEN TALKING TO A CHILD WHO WAS INJURED AT AN INCIDENT?

Tip – this is a very good question to prepare for. Not many candidates will be prepared for this. It is quite a difficult question to respond but do use the following pointers when constructing your response.

- Get on same level as the child. This could be achieved by crouching or sitting down.

- Change vocabulary to suit the age of the child. This is of particular importance as it will make the child more responsive. If you talk in an authoritarian tone then this will probably make the child go into his/her shell.

- Consider using the child's favourite toy to make them feel more secure.

- Consider using the parents/guardian as reassurance and a communication aid.

- Start off by getting the child to explain the problem. Do not always act on the parent's assumptions, as these could be wrong.

- If child does not speak to you, consider asking the parents to get the answers to the questions for you.

- If appropriate, explain the actions that you are taking in order to reassure the child.

- Possibly take off your formal uniform jacket to make the child feel more at ease.

- Calm the parents down; this will calm the overall situation down and help them to assist you in dealing with the child.

Q3 – CAN YOU TELL ME WHAT YOU KNOW ABOUT THE ROLE OF A PARAMEDIC?

(Sample response based on a Paramedic working for the London Ambulance Service)

Tip – this is a guaranteed question so make sure you are fully prepared for it. You can find out more about the role by visiting the NHS trust website and also by visiting an Ambulance Station and talking to the crew.

"Paramedics are the senior ambulance healthcare professionals at an accident or medical emergency, their main objective is to promote recovery and to preserve and protect life. Paramedics carry out emergency and non-emergency work. A crew on an ambulance usually consists of 2 paramedics or a paramedic and an EMT. When a paramedic arrives a scene, he will assess the situation, this will include carrying out dynamic risk assessments, he will then assess and diagnose each patient usually with a 12 lead life pack and administer drugs, oxygen or other life saving procedures like CPR or Defibrillation to make the patient stable enough to be conveyed to hospital where a full patient hand over would be given.

A patient report form and any other necessary paperwork would then need to be filled in before gearing up for the next job. The control room would be kept up to date with patient's movements and situations on scene. All treatment provided must be effective, safe and prompt and all patients should be treated excellent care, empathy and confidentiality.

Paramedics are trained to drive, what is effectively a mobile emergency room, based at an ambulance station with Duty Station Officers, Team Leaders, other A&E and PTS crews. As expected, the LAS are a 24/7 365 days a year service, and paramedics shifts would be rostered to cover that. It is also the responsibility of the paramedic on shift to ensure, his or her kit has been checked and is ready for use when needed and to make sure the vehicle is stocked, fuelled and cleaned both inside and out.

After the 3 year training period, paramedics would also have extra training classes and workshops and would be expected to top up skills and keep up to date with the latest policies and procedures."

Q4. HOW WOULD YOU CONTROL AN AGGRESSIVE AND CONFRONTATIONAL PERSON AT AN INCIDENT?

Tip – as a Paramedic you will need to deal with confrontational and aggressive people on many occasions. At no time should you ever put yourself in danger. The safety of yourself, your team and your equipment must always come first. You need to bear in mind that, on occasions when you are dealing people under the influence of alcohol, the Police may be a considerable time before attending. If you feel that any situation is become untenable, or that you are being placed in unnecessary danger, then you must always retreat. As a Paramedic you will learn how to carry out what is called a 'Dynamic Risk Assessment'. This will help you to determine how dangerous the situation is and what action you should take. Take a look at the following sample response.

"When dealing with conflict you need to think of the cycle of conflict, known as Betari's Box. This means that my attitude affects my behaviour which affects your attitude which affects your behaviour. That cycle carries on and the outcome is affected by the way you respond to the situation. Effective conflict management should be able to get a positive outcome and resolve the conflict. I have been in numerous situations like this through my previous roles as a bailiff and a door supervisor, most of which were successfully defused. When dealing with conflict, Dynamic risk assessments must always be taken. If all attempts to defuse the situation fail, retreat to somewhere safe and call for police assistance. Whilst working as a door supervisor in a city centre bar, I was made aware by a customer that there was an altercation between a member of bar staff and a customer. As I went to the bar, I could see that there was a person shouting and swearing at the bar staff and manager.

I walked up and asked the aggressor, which was the person shouting and swearing at the bar staff, what was the problem. His reply was "Go away, this has got nothing to do with you". My reply to the man was that I was the door supervisor and that it was something I had to deal with. His aggression then turned to me and he began to shout and swear at me. I adopted the Betari's box theory but remained assertive and used open hand hands whilst dealing with the situation. I didn't block the exit as he could have seen this as me trying to intimidate him and it could therefore cause a fight or flight situation. I said that I had been fair with him and wanted to talk outside to find out his version of what had gone on. When we were outside, away from the noise and his friends and the bar staff, he stated that he had given the bar man a £20 note but only given change from £10. I told him to wait outside and I would go and see the bar staff and try and sort the matter out.

After I had spoken to the bar man and the manager, they agreed that he did in fact give him a £20 note and was then given the correct change. I asked the bar man to come outside and speak to the man in order to explain what had happened. They both shook hands and both carried on with their nights. I feel that I dealt with the situation effectively. I could have gone into the situation with an aggressive attitude, which would have probably escalated the situation and just made matters worse. However, through effective conflict management, I was able to successfully defuse the situation."

Q5. WHY DO WE HAVE UNIFORM?

Tip – there are numerous benefits to wearing a uniform. Not only does it allow you to be easily identifiable to members of the public and other emergency crews, but is also affords you a level of protection from injury during incidents. Take a look at the following pointers which you should try to include in any response that you create.

- A uniform is a form of Personal Protective Equipment (PPE). Your helmet will protect you from falls and overhead objects. Your jacket will protect you from dirt, splashes and spillages. Your steel toe capped shoes/boots will protect your feet and your gloves will protect your hands from spillages and waste etc.

- A uniform is a sign of strength, authority and it gives reassurance to the public.

- A uniform brings the service together as one large team, regardless or beliefs and differences. This also demonstrates the equality and diversity of the Ambulance Service.

- The public also associate the green uniform with the ambulance service. This makes the Ambulance Service easily identifiable to the public, other emergency services and would also be a great benefit at a major incident. This principle is also adopted with HEMS in the orange flight suits.

- The helmet will protect you from falls and also overhead objects.

- Uniforms can also identify those people whom have senior rank. This is of particular importance at major incidents.

- A uniform is a sign of discipline within an organisation. It also requires pride to wear it which is a positive aspect.

Q6. WHY DO YOU WANT TO BECOME A PARAMEDIC?

Tip – once again this is a guaranteed question that you will need to prepare for. Think about the aspects of the role that involve working in the community, working with a diverse range of people, working for a professional organisation and having the chance to make a difference to your local community. Now take a look at the following sample response which will help you to construct your own.

"I feel that I have the necessary qualities that are required in order to become a paramedic. This is due to my previous roles as a Community First Responder, First Aider in the workplace and also as a plumber. I also have first hand experience of working in a diverse community.

Through hands on experience, reading books and talking to operational front line staff, I know that there is a high level of job satisfaction. I like helping make a difference to the people in the community at a time of need and enjoy interacting with the public and working in a customer service based role.

I am enthusiastic, punctual, well-disciplined and always strive for personal development and will enjoy undertaking a diverse role in a well disciplined and uniformed service, working closely with other emergency services and support agencies like St John ambulance."

Q7. WOULD YOU TREAT EVERYONE THE SAME OR DIFFERENTLY?

Tip – how you treat people both at work and in the community is important. You should always strive to treat people fairly, with respect and in a professional manner at all times. Remember that you are acting as a role model for the Ambulance Service and this should always come across in how you are with people whom your are serving. There are times, however, when you will need to treat people how they wish to be treated. Take a look at the following sample response which will give you some important tips and advice.

"Everyone should be treated the same and given the same high level of service. Regardless of my views or opinions, I think everyone deserves to be treated equal, however, sometimes things would need to be changed or altered to cater for the individual's needs. An example of this might me if I was called to a family's house whose religious faith means that they require me to take off my shoes before entering their home. In this instance I would follow my procedures and training and would carry out a risk assessment to determine whether this was safe to do so. If it was, then I would respect their wishes and remove my footwear.

I do believe that you should treat people how you expect to be treated yourself.

An example of this whilst working as a door supervisor, I would always treat everyone equal with empathy, courtesy and respect. On numerous occasions when I was being faced with rude and offensive behaviour towards me, I ignored it, but still remained resilient. There was an occasion when a disabled person in a wheelchair wanted to come into the bar I was working at, which is down a flight of stairs. My colleague told the guy in the wheelchair that he wasn't coming in and said nothing else. I had heard what he said and took the guy in the wheelchair to one side.

I apologised for my colleague's rudeness and explained that the reason we could not let him in was because in the event of a fire, he would not be able to get up the stairs unaided. This would cause a problem for us as it was out job to clear people out and we had other things that would need to be dealt with. After I explained this to him, he understood and agreed. I did speak to my colleague about the situation and told him that although we don't have to give reasons to people for refusal, in some circumstances like this one, I feel it is best.

By explaining this to the man in the wheelchair, he would see that it is purely for health and safety reasons and that he wasn't being discriminative towards him."

Q8. WHAT DO YOU THINK WILL BE THE BEST PARTS OF THE JOB?

Tip – this question is designed to assess your understanding of the role and it also gives the interviewer some idea of your intentions for joining. If you tell the panel that the best parts of the job are "Speeding down the road in an Ambulance with lights and sirens going" or "Dealing with injuries and fatalities" then you are going to score very low for this question. Take a look at the following bullet points which will give you some great pointers for responding to this question.

- Helping the local community and educating them in resuscitation and first aid.
- Improving people's lives, well-being and in extreme situations, saving lives.
- Being a role model for the Ambulance Service.
- Working with a professional and diverse group of people.
- Making a difference to the community in which I am working within.
- Learning new skills.
- Continually improving and developing as a person.
- The shift work. Not having to work in a regular 9-5 job can be very appealing to some people. (Please see the next question for how shift work can be negative.)
- Looking after your equipment and making sure that it is ready for operational use.
- Learning procedures and continually training to be prepared for every eventuality.
- Working with the other emergency services.
- Providing reassurance to the community not only physically but also mentally. The people we serve will feel safe and comforted knowing we are here when they need us.

Q9. WHAT DO YOU THINK WILL BE THE BAD POINTS ABOUT THE JOB?

Tip – you obviously need to be careful when responding to this question, simply because there are some aspects to this role that cannot be avoided. For example, if you state that "seeing blood" makes you feel uneasy, then you are not going to make it through the interview. Be careful when responding to the interview and use the following pointers as a guide to assisting you in your preparation.

- The shift patterns will have a big impact on your life and could be both mentally and physically demanding at times. Therefore you will require a level of resilience.

- Being in a position where you are not able to help someone or prevent the situation worsening.

- Not getting to people in time due to traffic congestion and people failing to move out of the way when you are responding to an incident under blue light conditions.

- Cars that are parked illegally that could hinder an emergency vehicle getting through.

- Hoax callers that waste time and also cost lives.

Q10. WHY DO YOU WANT TO WORK FOR THE AMBULANCE SERVICE?

Tip – only you will know the answer to this question and it needs to be based on your own feelings and ambitions. Take a look the following pointers before reading the sample response which is based on an applicant wishing to join the London Ambulance Service.

- To be in a role where I can make a difference to people's lives and to society as a whole.
- To work as a part of a professional, disciplined and organised workforce.
- To have some structure to my life.
- To have the opportunity to develop and progress.
- To be able to act as a role model for the service.

"I enjoy interacting with people from diverse backgrounds and working in a customer service based role. I have first hand knowledge of how the trust operates from my voluntary role as a CFR and I have been on numerous ride outs with paramedics, team leaders and duty station officers. I have a good understanding of the way that LAS operates, both from a clinical aspect and from a management point of view. The prospect of progression through the ranks after obtaining experience as a paramedic really excites me. I have wanted to become a paramedic from a young age and decided to join the LAS as it's the biggest in the world. It has over 4500 employees and serves a diverse 620 square mile area, answering nearly 3000 calls a day."

Q11. WHAT LEARNING TECHNIQUES WOULD YOU USE DURING YOUR INITIAL PARAMEDIC TRAINING COURSE?

Tip – the training course for becoming a paramedic is arduous and tough. You will need to persuade the interview panel that you have what it takes to pass it. Providing examples of where you have recently attended and passed a training course would be beneficial. Take a look at the following sample response which will give you some tips and idea on how to create a good response to this type of question.

"Over the last few years I have developed my skills and qualifications in computers, first aid and obtaining my C1. I have also completed a First Aid at Work Assessors course. I have spent numerous hours at home revising and searching the internet for more in-depth subject knowledge. I am a visual and kinaesthetic learner, drawing pictures and mind maps help me when dealing with an in-depth subject. I summarise the subject in notes which I can read over to jog my memory if needed.

With regards to the paramedic training, I will adopt the same way of learning and will continue my study at home with the use of the internet if needed. I also have some friends who are in the medical profession who I could ask for help and guidance if needed."

Q12. WHAT WOULD YOU DO IF SOMEONE ASKED YOU TO TAKE YOUR SHOES OFF IN THEIR HOUSE?

Tip – this subject has already been covered in a previous question. However, take a look at the following tips which will help you to understand how to react to this type of request.

- Be sympathetic towards their request if possible. Their reason for asking could be for religious reason. If it is for religious reasons then I would carry out a risk assessment and decide whether it was possible or not. I would always follow my training and procedural guidance.

- I would explain that I have to wear my shoes/boots for health and safety reasons.

- I would also explain that if I did take my shoes off this would delay me in reaching the patient and this would affect me being effective, safe and prompt.

- If available I would wear overshoes or ask if the patient could be assessed and treated in the ambulance.

Q13. WHAT WOULD YOU DO DIFFERENTLY WHEN TREATING A MEMBER OF THE OPPOSITE SEX?

Tip – when treating a member of the opposite sex you will need to follow procedures and training at all times. You will need to be respectful, especially when removing clothing or items which may make the person feel uncomfortable or vulnerable. Take a look at the following tips and pointers which will help you to create a solid response to this question.

- Continue as normal but ask the patient if he/she is ok to be treated by a Paramedic of the opposite sex. I would always be respectful of the patient's wishes.

- Fully explain what I intend to do and get permission before giving any treatment.

- If I was treating a female patient, and I had a female crew mate with me, it may make the patient feel more at ease if she were to take over in that situation.

- It would be beneficial to go out in a mixed crew when the opportunity arises so as to avoid any problems.

Q14. WHAT WOULD YOU DO IF A COLLEAGUE DID SOMETHING THAT YOU DIDN'T AGREE WITH OR THAT WAS AGAINST ORGANISATIONAL PROCEDURES?

Tip – organisational procedures are there for a reason. They prevent accidents, injuries to others and also prevent employees from falling foul of the law. It is important that they are followed and implemented at all times. Take a look at the following sample response which will assist you in creating your own response based on your own views.

"If it was a life threatening situation then I would have to challenge it straight away. If it was not serious and the incident occurred in front of a patient, I would ask to speak to my colleague outside or away from the incident in private and in confidence.

If we had situation and it was not sufficiently serious then management would not necessarily need to be involved. This would depend on the severity of the incident.

Unless life threatening, I feel any disagreements should always be dealt with away from public view. If they were done in public view, or the patient heard the disagreement, I would not give a very good impression of the service. It also doesn't give a professional image that I like to give whilst carrying out my duties.

If the situation was serious, or it involved an illegal practice, then I would stop it immediately and inform my supervisory manager."

Q15. WHY DOES THE AMBULANCE SERVICE HAVE SO MANY POLICIES?

Tip – policies are there to provide employees with guidance and protocol which they must follow. If an organisation such as the Ambulance Service did not have such policies then people would become injured or worse. Take a look at the following sample response which will provide you with a number of useful tips and advice.

"Policies are in place to safeguard practice, staff and the public we serve. They also create a corporate approach and response. As you can imagine, the Ambulance Service may perform 10 or 20 procedures on each patient, then convey them in a speeding ambulance in a busy city centre. There would be policies of how to perform certain things and policies for what to do when things go wrong.

There will also be policies that will meet national standards and all policies must be adhered to at all times. If someone deviates from policies, it could cost public and crew lives, money, employment termination and the Ambulance Services reputation.

Some of the policies in force include, use of drugs, use of equipment, incident procedures, major incidents, harassment and bullying, equality and diversity, disciplinary procedures and REAP level procedures etc."

Q16. WHY DO WE WANT THE AMBULANCE SERVICE TO BE DIVERSE?

Tip – any public service must be diverse in order to represent the community in which it serves. Society is diverse in nature and therefore it is only right that all public services are representative of the community. For example, there are many groups of people in our society that do not speak English. Therefore, it is only right that the service employs staff who are capable of speaking certain languages and also understanding different groups needs and requirements. Take a look at the following sample response.

"Society is a very diverse place. It has people from all over the world of different ages and capabilities from the poor to the rich and different religious beliefs and sexual preference. The Ambulance Service must reflect this by employing people from diverse backgrounds. It also sets an example that other people and businesses will hopefully follow. This also shows leadership from the Ambulance Service. I feel it is important to show the public that you are diverse as an organisation. If the Ambulance Service were not diverse, maybe people from different cultures or that have less capabilities would not ring for help when needed and this goes against the trusts vision and values."

Q17. WHY DO YOU WANT TO JOIN THIS PARTICULAR AMBULANCE SERVICE AND WHAT DO YOU HAVE TO OFFER?

This type of question is extremely common so your response should be prepared beforehand.

The type of information you provide in your response needs to focus on the job description and the vision statement of the particular service you are applying to join. Remember that the Ambulance Service is exactly that – 'a service'.

The London Ambulance Service's vision is as follows – 'A world-class ambulance service for London staffed by well-trained, enthusiastic and proud people who are all recognised for contributing to the provision of high-quality patient care'.

Look at the vision statement of the service you are applying to join and you will find some useful tips here to help you structure your response.

Sample response

"I have always been interested in this type of work, where caring for the needs of others is a priority. I understand that the job is demanding and stressful at times but the satisfaction of working in a close knit team that helps others in need is something that very much appeals to me. Having looked into this particular service, I am impressed by the standards it sets itself. I am a self-disciplined, trusted and enthusiastic person who would thrive in such a role, where serving our diverse community is its main aim.

My previous experience of working in a customer-based role has given me a good foundation for this type of work. I have experience of dealing with difficult situations and have the maturity and ability to diffuse conflict situations when the need arises. I am hard working, reliable and committed in everything I do and believe I would be a great asset to your already successful team. I also keep myself physically fit and active and understand that the role of emergency medical technician is demanding.

Finally, I have read and understand the vision statement of this Ambulance Service. I believe I have the commitment and motivation to abide by these important standards and would very much thrive in a professional organisation where teamwork and self discipline are of great importance."

Q18. GIVE AN EXAMPLE OF WHERE YOU HAVE HAD TO DEAL WITH A MEMBER OF THE PUBLIC IN A POTENTIAL CONFLICT SITUATION (VIOLENT, DRUNK, ANGRY ETC). HOW DID YOU ATTEMPT TO TAKE CONTROL OF THE SITUATION?

This type of question is designed to assess your emotional maturity and assertiveness. Whilst working as a paramedic or emergency care assistant you may face difficult situations where some members of the public are under the influence of alcohol and acting in a violent manner. When answering this type of question you must give a response that demonstrates how you have dealt with similar situations in the past. It will not be good enough just to tell them how you 'would' deal with this situation if it arose but moreover how you 'have' dealt with this type of situation in the past.

Sample response

"Whilst working in my current role as a customer service manager I was faced with an angry customer who was dissatisfied with the level of service he had received from our shop. He had purchased a pair of shoes for his daughter's birthday but when she went to open the shoes she found that they were both of a different size. The shop assistant had made a mistake and should have checked the shoe sizes before selling them to the gentleman. Unfortunately, when I tried to apologise for our error and offer a full refund along with a new pair of shoes for his daughter, he refused to calm down and continued to act in an angry manner. I knew that it was important for me to remain calm and not respond to his aggression. If I had responded in a similar aggressive manner I would have been making the situation worse, so I decided to stay calm and talk to him in a mild-mannered voice, asking him politely not to shout at me. Unfortunately, he did not calm down. Instead, he began to swear and threaten me, suggesting that the member of staff who made the mistake should be sacked immediately and if I didn't do this, I would be in trouble. I then decided to give him a warning that if he didn't calm down and stop swearing, the Police would be called. He did not listen to me, so I walked away from the confrontational situation and telephoned the Police. As soon as he saw me calling the Police the man left the shop. Although he had left the shop I still asked for the Police to attend due to the threatening behaviour. When the Police arrived I gave a statement and requested that *the matter be investigated.*

I believe it is important to provide an excellent level of service to our customers but that does not mean that you should accept any form of verbal or physical abuse. I would never respond aggressively to any such situation. Instead I would always walk away from a situation like this and inform the relevant authorities."

Q19. WHAT DIFFERENT TACTICS MIGHT YOU USE TO AVOID A CONFRONTATIONAL SITUATION?

This type of question is designed to assess your ability to diffuse potentially difficult and confrontational situations.

Always remember that, whilst you should be assertive, it is unacceptable to become aggressive or confrontational yourself. This will just make the situation worse and do nothing to diffuse the situation. You must also have the common sense to realise that when a situation is becoming dangerous you need to walk away and protect both yourself and your colleagues.

Whilst working as a paramedic or emergency care assistant you will be dealing with people who are under the influence of alcohol and therefore have the potential to become aggressive.

When responding to these types of question try to show your knowledge of different tactics that can be employed to diffuse confrontational situations. It is worth mentioning that you will use the training that you are given by the Ambulance Service to avoid confrontational situations.

Sample response

"To begin with, probably the most important factor is to remember not to respond in a similar, confrontational manner. This will only make the situation worse. I believe it is important not to be intimidated by such behaviour and there is a level of assertiveness that must be applied. I would try to talk to the individual in a calm manner, trying to establish a rapport with them. I would ask them what their name was and ask them some questions to try to diffuse the situation. I would try to use both verbal and non-verbal communication skills to avoid a confrontational situation including body language that is non-aggressive. I would listen to what they were saying and try to verbally intervene at an appropriate time, asking questions about how they felt and calling them by their first name if possible. If I could get the person to sit down and try to relax this would help to diffuse the situation. Talking to them in a calm manner is important. However, if I were unable to diffuse a confrontational situation, I would know when to walk away and ask for assistance. The safety of myself and my work colleagues is paramount."

Q20. WHY DO YOU THINK THE AMBULANCE SERVICE PUTS SO MUCH IMPORTANCE UPON DIVERSITY AND COMMUNITY AWARENESS?

This type of question is again looking to assess your ability to interact effectively with people from diverse backgrounds.

In order to provide the highest level of service, a public service such as the Ambulance Service must be as diverse as the community in which it serves.

Once again, it is advisable to be aware of the Race Equality Scheme for the service you are applying to join.

The Ambulance Service must understand the needs of its community in order to provide the highest level of service. This can only be achieved through a process of continuous development and learning. By interacting with the community and responding to its needs, the Ambulance Service will continue to improve and develop. Make sure you understand the importance of diversity, but more importantly believe in it!

Sample response

"For the simple reason that the community in which it serves is diverse in nature and therefore requires a service that is both understanding, culturally aware, responsive to its needs and willing to learn. If the community in which we live is diverse, then the public services that represent it should be too. In terms of community awareness, the Ambulance Service must understand the needs of the community in which it serves.

It should be aware of the different cultures and backgrounds of its community, so that it can be respectful and understand the needs of everyone in society. By doing this it will be able to provide the highest level of service to the people it serves.

If the Ambulance Service is not aware of the community it cares for then it cannot continually improve and provide the highest level of service to everyone."

Q21. CAN YOU PROVIDE AN EXAMPLE OF WHEN YOU HAVE WORKED AS PART OF A TEAM TO ACHIEVE A GOAL?

Having the ability to work as part of a team is very important to the role of a paramedic and emergency care assistant. Ambulance Services employ many people in different roles, from 999 call operators to vehicle mechanics to administrative workers. In fact, it is not uncommon for thousands of people to work for one particular service. As an example, there are over 4000 people working for the London Ambulance Service! Therefore, it is essential that every member of the team works together in order to achieve the ultimate goal of providing a high quality level of patient care.

The recruitment staff will want to be certain that you can work effectively as part of a team, which is why you may be asked questions that relate to your team-working experience. Not only should you be capable of working effectively with other paramedics but also with other workers within the service and outside of it.

Sample response

"Yes, I can. I like to keep fit and healthy and as part of this aim I play football for a local Sunday team. We had worked very hard to get to the cup final and we were faced with playing a very good opposition team who had recently won the league title. After only ten minutes of play, one of our players was sent off and we conceded a penalty as a result. Being one goal down and 80 minutes left to play we were faced with a mountain to climb.

However, we all remembered our training and worked very hard in order to prevent any more goals being scored. Due to playing with ten players, I had to switch positions and play as a defender, something that I am not used to. The team worked brilliantly to hold off any further opposing goals and after 60 minutes we managed to get an equaliser. The game went to penalties in the end and we managed to win the cup.

I believe I am an excellent team player and can always be relied upon to work as an effective team member at all times. I understand that being an effective team member is very important if the Ambulance Service is to provide a high level of service to the community that it serves. Part of the role of a paramedic includes working with other teams, both within the service and also outside it, such as the Police and Fire Service."

Q22. CAN YOU PROVIDE AN EXAMPLE OF A SITUATION WHEN YOU HAVE HAD TO WORK UNDER PRESSURE?

The role of a paramedic will often requirement to work under extreme pressure. Therefore, the recruitment staff will want to know that you have the ability to perform in such an environment. If you already have experience of working under pressure then you are far more likely to succeed as a paramedic and be capable of meeting the demands of the job. When responding to a question of this nature, try to provide an actual example of where you have achieved a task whilst being under pressure. Don't forget to follow the guidance at the beginning of this section, which related to responding effectively to 'situational' interview questions.

Questions of this nature are sometimes included in the application form, so try to use a different example for the interview, if the question comes up.

Sample response

"Yes, I can. In my current job as car mechanic for a well-known company, I was presented with a difficult and pressurised situation. A member of the team had made a mistake and had fitted a number of wrong components to a car. The car in question was due to be picked up at 2pm and the customer had stated how important it was that his car was ready on time because he had an important meeting to attend. We only had two hours in which to resolve the issue and I volunteered to be the one who would carry out the work on the car. The problem was that we had 3 other customers in the workshop waiting for their cars too, so I was the only person who could be spared at that particular time.

I worked solidly for the next 2 hours, making sure that I meticulously carried out each task in line with our operating procedures. Even though I didn't finish the car until 2.10pm, I managed to achieve a very difficult task under pressurised conditions whilst following strict procedures and regulations. I understand that the role of a paramedic will require me to work under extreme pressure at times and I believe I have the experience to achieve this. I am very meticulous in my work and always ensure that I take personal responsibility to keep up to date with procedures and policies in my current job."

Q23. WHAT SKILLS DO YOU POSSESS THAT YOU THINK WOULD BE AN ASSET TO OUR ORGANISATION?

When responding to questions of this nature, try to match your skills with the skills that are required of a paramedic. On some Ambulance Service websites you will be able to read about the type of person they are looking to employ, usually in the recruitment section. An example of this would be:

'We are looking for highly organised and caring team players who are of a compassionate disposition. You will possess a good level of manual dexterity and be capable of upholding the principles of our organisation whilst providing a high level of patient care to the people whom we serve.'

Just by looking at the Ambulance Service's website, you should be able to obtain some clues as to the type of person they are seeking to employ. It is also worthwhile studying the job description and person specification, as these will also provide details of the type of person they are looking to employ. Try to think of the skills that are required to perform the role you are applying for and include them in your response.

Sample response

"I am a very conscientious person who takes the time to learn and develop new skills correctly. I have vast experience working in a customer-focused environment and fully understand that excellent patient care is important. It is important that every member of the team works towards providing a high level of service. I believe I have the skills, knowledge and experience to do this. I am a very good team player and can always be relied upon to carry out my role to the highest of standards. I am a flexible person and understand that there is a need to be available at short notice to cover duties if required. In addition to these skills and attributes, I am a very good communicator and understand that different members of the community will need a different approach.

For example, when dealing with elderly members of the community I will have to be very patient and cater for their needs in a more sensitive manner. I am highly safety conscious and have a health and safety qualification to my name. Therefore, I can be relied upon to perform all procedures correctly and in line with my training and will not put others or myself in any danger whatsoever.

Finally, I am very good at learning new skills, which means that I will work hard to pass all of my continuation training if I am successful in becoming a paramedic."

Q24. CAN YOU PROVIDE US WITH AN EXAMPLE OF A SAFETY-RELATED TASK THAT YOU HAVE HAD TO PERFORM?

Safety is an extremely important part of the paramedic's role, and the recruitment staff need to know that you are capable of working safely at all times. The term 'safety' should be an integral part of your responses during the interview. Making reference to the fact that you are aware of the importance of safety is a positive thing.

When responding to safety-related questions you should try to include examples where you have had to work to, or follow, safety guidelines or procedures. If you have a safety qualification then it is definitely worthwhile mentioning this during your interview. Any relevant safety experience or safety-related role should also be discussed.

Sample response

"I currently work as a gas fitter and I am often required to perform safety-related tasks. An example of one of these tasks would involve the installation of gas-fired boilers. When fitting a gas boiler, I have to ensure that I carry out a number of safety checks during the installation stage, which ensures my work is safe and to a high standard.

In addition to carrying out work in line with procedures and regulations, I also carry out daily checks on my equipment to ensure that it is serviceable, operational and safe. If I find any problems then I immediately take steps to get the equipment repaired by a qualified engineer or technician.

I have been trained, and I am qualified, to carry out my work in accordance with strict safety guidelines. I also have a number of safety certificates to demonstrate my competence.

I am fully aware that if I do not carry out my job in accordance with safety guidelines there is the possibility that somebody may be injured or even killed."

FURTHER SAMPLE GENERIC INTERVIEW QUESTIONS

Now that we have completed studying the types of possible interview questions you may be asked, I will provide you with a number of generic interview questions that you may be asked during the paramedic interview.

Please note I have not provided sample responses to these questions, as the response you provide must be solely based around your own skills, knowledge and experience.

SAMPLE GENERIC INTERVIEW QUESTION NUMBER 1

Can you provide us with an example of when you have had to work in an emergency?

This question is also likely to be asked during the application form stage of the process. Being able to remain calm under pressure is very important and will form an integral part of your training. Maybe you have had to deal with an emergency at work or even in the home?

Whatever example you decide to use, make sure you tell the interviewers that you stayed calm and focused on the task in hand. Make reference to the importance of safety during your response too.

SAMPLE GENERIC INTERVIEW QUESTION NUMBER 2

Do you think you would get bored of routine tasks such as checking your equipment and reading up on procedures etc?

Of course the only answer here is no. Part of the job of a paramedic and emergency care assistant is to check and familiarise yourself with your equipment and keep up to date with procedures. Every job has mundane tasks but it is usually these tasks that are the most important.

SAMPLE GENERIC INTERVIEW QUESTION NUMBER 3

How many people work for this organisation and where are the ambulance stations located?

Questions that relate to facts and figures or the structure of the service are commonplace. The panel will want to know that you are serious about joining their Ambulance Service and that you have looked into their organisation in detail. Make sure you study the organisation, the people and its structure before you attend the interview. You will be able to find plenty of information on the service's website.

SAMPLE GENERIC INTERVIEW QUESTION NUMBER 4

What are the vision/mission and aims of this company?

Many organisations, including Ambulance Services and NHS Trusts, set themselves aims and objectives. They will also have a vision or mission statement and a patient charter. These usually relate to the high level of customer service and patient care that they promise to deliver. When you apply to become a paramedic or emergency care assistant you should study these important documents and be able to recite them. It will look good in your interview if you can explain in detail what these involve. Learning this kind of information is important and it will put you ahead of the competition.

Always remember this rule – Working for the Trust comes first, becoming a paramedic comes second! Visit the website of the Trust in order to view their mission, aims, objectives or patient charter.

SAMPLE GENERIC INTERVIEW QUESTION NUMBER 5

How do you think you would cope with working under strenuous conditions for long periods of time?

Paramedics are often required to work under difficult conditions for lengthy periods of time. You will attend many road traffic collisions during your time, where your skills, stamina and professionalism will be tested to the limit. Can you cope with it? Do you have any experience of working under these types of conditions? If you do have experiences in this area then try to provide an example when responding to this question.

SAMPLE GENERIC INTERVIEW QUESTION NUMBER 6

What is your sickness record like and what do you think is an acceptable level of sickness?

The Ambulance Service wants to employ people who have good sickness records. Your attendance at work is integral to the smooth running of the ambulance station. When you go off work sick, it affects the other team members, as somebody will have to cover. Basically no amount of sickness is acceptable but obviously genuine sickness cannot be helped. Remember to tell the panel that you do not take time off sick unless absolutely necessary and you can be relied upon to come to work.

SAMPLE GENERIC INTERVIEW QUESTION NUMBER 7

Have you ever worked during the night and how do you feel about working shifts?

The work of a paramedic involves irregular shift patterns and the Ambulance Service will want to know that you can handle them. Speak to any person who works shifts and they will tell you that after a number of years they can start to take their toll. Remember to tell the panel that you are looking forward to working shifts and, in particular, night duties. If you can provide examples of where you have worked irregular shift patterns then remember to tell them as this will work in your favour. It may also be advisable to tell the panel that your family fully support you in your application and they appreciate the impact working shifts may have on your home and social life.

SAMPLE GENERIC INTERVIEW QUESTION NUMBER 8

Can you provide us with an example of a project you have had to complete and the obstacles you had to overcome?

Having the ability to complete tasks and projects successfully demonstrates that you have the ability to complete your paramedic/ ambulance technician training.

Many people give up on things in life and they fail to achieve their goals. The recruitment staff will want to know that you are going to complete all of your training successfully and, if you can provide evidence of where you have already done this, then this will go in your favour.

When responding to this type of question, try to think of a difficult, long drawn-out task that you achieved despite a number of obstacles that were in your way.

THE PARAMEDIC DEGREE INTERVIEW

Students who wish to enrol on a paramedic degree course will be required to pass a selection process that includes an interview. It is the interview that the majority of candidates are concerned with, as they need to successfully convince the panel that they should choose them to embark on the paramedic science degree course.

The interview panel will normally consist of a university course tutor and a paramedic. The member of the panel who is from the university will be primarily interested in assessing whether or not you have the ability to successfully pass the course, while the paramedic will be more concerned with whether or not you possess the right skills to become a paramedic.

In the build-up to the paramedic science degree interview you should concentrate your preparation on the following main areas:

- How you would react to certain emergency incidents.
- The role of a paramedic and the ambulance service.
- Why you want to become a paramedic.
- Why you think you can successfully pass the course.
- Issues that are affecting the NHS and the ambulance service at that particular time.

In order to help you prepare more effectively, we will now take a look at each area in detail and, more importantly, the reasons why the panel want to know this information.

HOW YOU WOULD REACT TO CERTAIN EMERGENCY INCIDENTS

As you can imagine, part of the role of the paramedic is having the ability to remain calm during extremely testing incidents. The interview panel, especially the paramedic, will be interested to see how you react to certain emergency incidents.

The majority of students who apply to become a paramedic will have hopefully never witnessed a fatality, so therefore they will need to provide an explanation of how they believe they would act in such a situation.

When preparing for this type of question think about how you would react in any of the following scenarios:

Scenario 1

How do you think you would react if you were the first person to arrive at the scene of a serious road traffic collision?

Things to consider

- It is important that paramedics remain calm at all times whilst attending emergency incidents. If they are calm then they are in control and they will therefore be able to perform their duties competently and professionally.

- Whilst attending road traffic collisions paramedics and other members of the emergency services need to carry out a 'dynamic risk assessment' (DRA). In basic terms, the DRA is the management of risk through a continuous process of identifying hazards, assessing risks, taking action to eliminate or reduce risk, monitoring and reviewing, all in the rapidly changing circumstances of the operational incident. It is their responsibility to ensure that they and other people at the scene are safe.

- Patient care is vitally important. Assessing the needs of each of the casualties and providing the appropriate level of care would be the task of the paramedic.

Scenario 2

As a paramedic you receive a 999 call to an incident at a nightclub. A man has been attacked and his attacker has left the scene. What would you do?

Things to consider

- One of the first priorities, in addition to patient care, would be to request the attendance of the police. They would need to attend in order to gather details of the alleged attack and also to provide you with support and protection whilst you treat the injured.

- Again, you would need to carry out a dynamic risk assessment of the scene to ensure that you are safe.

- At all times you must remain calm. During incidents where alcohol is involved, those under the influence may act in an aggressive, violent or confrontational manner and you would need to ensure that your exit is maintained at all times.

- During incidents of this nature you may also be required to calm people down and create space so that you can attend to the casualty. During such incidents onlookers tend to gather, which can impede your ability as a paramedic to treat the patient.

THE ROLE OF A PARAMEDIC AND THE AMBULANCE SERVICE

You can learn a lot about the role of a paramedic by visiting the website of the NHS trust you wish to join.

Things to consider

- Take a look at the website of the ambulance service or NHS trust that you are interested in joining if you successfully pass the paramedic science degree course. What does it say about the role and what does it say about the ambulance service.

- Consider learning the vision and the values of the service. The panel will be impressed if you are able to recite these.

- Try to arrange a visit at your local ambulance station and ask the paramedics about their role and what it involves.

WHY YOU WANT TO BECOME A PARAMEDIC

Only you will know the reason why you want to become a paramedic. When considering your response to questions based around this theme, try to think about the qualities of a paramedic that you are able to match. Keep away from reasons such as salary, pension and the opportunity to drive around in an ambulance with the blue lights flashing!

Things to consider

The positive aspects of the role include:

- The chance to make a difference.

- Working with a highly professional team of people.

- The opportunity to work within a diverse workforce and a diverse community.

- Learning new skills and obtaining qualifications.
- Working in a job where no two days are the same – the variety of the job.

WHY YOU THINK YOU CAN SUCCESSFULLY PASS THE COURSE

Those candidates who can demonstrate they have previous history of successfully completing difficult tasks and training courses are far more likely to stick with the degree course and pass it.

During the interview the panel may ask you to explain why you think you can successfully pass the paramedic science degree course. During your response it is important that you can provide details of where you have previously worked hard in order to gain a qualification or complete a training course. You will most probably have studied hard previously to pass either your GCSEs or A-Levels and this evidence should form the basis of your response.

The panel will also want to see a demonstration of enthusiasm and passion from you, as this will provide further evidence of your commitment to successfully completing the course.

Questions of this nature are usually designed to separate those candidates who are genuinely interested and passionate about becoming a paramedic from those who are simply going through the motions and have not put any real thought into their chosen course or career path.

Things to consider

- Provide details of where you have previously studied over a long period of time and obtained some form of qualification.
- Demonstrate a level of passion and enthusiasm for the course and for the role of a paramedic.
- Provide evidence of where you have gone out of your way to find out about the course and also the role of a paramedic.

ISSUES THAT ARE AFFECTING THE NHS AND THE AMBULANCE SERVICE AT THAT PARTICULAR TIME

At any particular time there will be certain issues affecting the NHS. For example, at the time of writing this guide one of the most important issues affecting the NHS is that of 'swine flu' and how the government and the NHS aim to tackle the problem and prevent its spread.

The reason why the panel ask this type of question is to assess whether or not you have a genuine interest in the NHS and the Ambulance Service.

Make sure you keep up to date with current affairs that are affecting the NHS, the role of a paramedic and the Ambulance Service.

Things to consider

- In the build-up to your interview visit websites and chat forums on the internet to learn what the current topical issues are that are affecting the NHS.

- Consider subscribing to a paramedic journal or magazine, as these will usually contain up-to-date issues and current affairs.

FURTHER TIPS AND ADVICE FOR PREPARING FOR THE PARAMEDIC INTERVIEW

- The interviewers may ask you more generic questions relating to your past experiences or skills. These may be in relation to how you solve problems, your strengths and weaknesses, team-working skills, communication skills and questions that relate to the physical aspects of the role. Make sure you have examples for each of these.

- Try to speak to a current serving paramedic or emergency care assistant of the service that you are applying to join. Ask him/her what it is like to work for that particular service and what current issues they are facing.

- Try to think of a time when you have made a mistake and how you learnt from the experience. The panel may ask you questions that relate to how you deal with setbacks in your life.

- When you complete the application form, make sure you keep a copy of it. Before you go to your interview ensure that you read the application form over and over again as you may find you are asked questions about your responses.

- Don't be afraid to ask the interviewer to repeat a question if you do not hear it the first time. Take your time when answering and be measured in your responses.

- If you don't know the answer to a question then be honest and just say 'I don't know'. This is far better than trying to answer a question that you have no knowledge about. Conversely, if your answer to a question is challenged, there is nothing wrong with sticking to your point but make sure you acknowledge the interviewer's thoughts or views. Be polite and never get into a debate.

- When you walk into the interview room stand up straight and introduce yourself. Be polite and courteous at all times and try to come across in a pleasant manner. The panel will be assessing you as soon as you walk through the door so make sure you make a positive first impression.

- Do not sit down in the interview chair until you are invited to do so. This is good manners.

- When you sit down in the interview chair, sit upright and do not fidget or slouch. It is acceptable to use hand gestures when explaining your responses to the questions but don't overdo it, as this can become a distraction.

- Structure your responses to the questions in a logical manner – this is very important. When responding to an interview question start at the beginning and work your way through in a concise manner, and at a pace that is easy for the panel to listen to.

- Speak clearly and at a tone that is easy for the panel to hear. Be confident in your responses.

- When talking to the panel use eye contact but be careful not to look at them in an intimidating manner.

- Consider wearing some form of formal outfit to the interview such as a suit. Whilst you will not be assessed on the type of outfit you wear to the interview, it will make you come across in a more professional manner. Remember that you are applying to join a uniformed service.

how2become

Visit www.how2become.co.uk to find more titles and courses that will help you to pass the paramedic selection process, including:

- How to pass the paramedic interview DVD

- 1-day paramedic training course.

- Online paramedic psychometric testing.

- Psychometric testing books and CD's

www.how2become.co.uk